MMO CD
4111
MMO Cass.
8021

MUSIC MINUS ONE
BEGINNING
CONTEST SOLOS

LAUREATE SERIES

ALTO
SAXOPHONE
MUSIC BOOK

GAVOTTE
from "Clavier Suite in G Minor"

JOHANN SEBASTIAN BACH

Allegretto

AVE VERUM

WOLFGANG A. MOZART
Arr. by Sigurd Rascher

Adagio
Piano
Solo

HUNTERS CHORUS

CARL MARIA VON WEBER
Arr. by Sigurd Rascher

Lively
Piano
Solo

ANDANTE

JOSEPH HAYDN

Andante
Piano
Solo

INTERMEZZO
from "L'Arlesienne Suite No. 2"

GEORGES BIZET
Trans. By Harry Gee
Edited by Don McCathren

Andante moderato, ma con moto
Piano
Solo

LARGO

CHOPIN
Trans. by E. Rousseau

dolce cantabile

ALBUM LEAF

EDWARD GRIEG

LARGHETTO

ANTONIN DVOŘÁK

Larghetto

EVENING WALTZ

A. GRETCHANINOFF, Op. 145, No. 10
Trans. By H. Voxman

Tempo di Valse; moderato

RONDINO

FRITZ KREISLER
Arr. By Cecil Leeson

Allegro grasioso

PERFORMANCE GUIDE
COMMENTARY BY PAUL BRODIE

BACH
Clavier Suite in G Minor
Gavotte

Although you may wish to practice this piece in an easy four, it must be performed in cut time, at brisk tempo. The dynamic contrasts are well marked, and very effective. You will find the use of a legato tongue most helpful. There are many places for a B flat fingering; of the several possibilites, the bis fingering is perhaps the best.

MOZART
Ave verum, K. 618

This Motet was one of Mozart's last compositions. It must be very sustained. If you need an extra breath, be careful that you don't interrupt the flow of music. Dynamics must be subtle; this music does not need dramatic accentuation. Sing through your instrument in a *bel canto* style, and remember that this piece was originally intended for use in a church!

VON WEBER
Der Freischuetz
Hunters' Chorus

When you begin to study this piece, you should ignore the musical and dynamic aspects, and learn it from a technical standpoint. After you have all the notes and the correct articulation, you can begin to play it up to tempo and try to interpret it musically. Try to get a crisp, martial spirit.

The breathing places as marked are quite adequate. Be careful not to rush the sixteenth notes; you must be exactly in time with the accompaniment. If you have difficulty in tonguing quickly, feel free to change the articulation. Since this is a transcription of a vocal piece, the original articulation was probably much different.

HAYDN
Violin Sonata No. 1
Andante

Begin this piece very slowly, and with a smooth legato. When you are able to play it up to tempo, the legato will become a light staccato. Notice the grace note in measure 41:

Do not rush the sixteenth notes in measure 57. Even though there are staccato markings here, these notes must not be too detached! When you play the loud accents in the last bar, you must be careful not to change your embouchure!

BIZET
L'Arlesienne Suite No. 2
Intermezzo

Notice the "hairpins" (crescendo and decrescendo) in the opening phrases. These inflections are necessary to a successful performance of this piece. Do not exaggerate the ritard in measure 15. The accompaniment sets the tempo in measure 16, and the new tempo should not be too different from the opening *Andante moderato*. Notice how the tempo has been modified with the words, *ma con moto* (but with motion)!

There are several *sforzandos* in this piece (measures 25, 37, and 38). Although *sforzando* means "suddenly loud," you must not press your tone so hard that it looses its beauty. Try the upper octave in measure 39; it seems to add greatly to the lyricism of this piece. You will want good strong accents in measure 44.

This piece has several sections where you can use your side C fingering. (Use side C whenever you have a B natural going to a C natural.) If the note tends to be flat, then of course you'll have to use your regular fingering.

CHOPIN
Largo

This music was transcribed for me by Eugene Rousseau. People are sometimes snobbish about the use of transcriptions. I don't think any composer would mind his music being played on another instrument as long as his style is retained. In the days of the great classic composers such as Mozart, violin sonatas were performed on harmonicas, water glasses, and bells. We are not blessed with original compositions by Bach, Beethoven, and Brahms. Therefore, transcriptions are necessary if we are going to have a well-rounded repertoire. *But be careful to play them in the style of the composer!*

This music shows all the qualities of the saxophone. It was originally a piece for 'cello, and it is *dolce* and *cantabile,* a very warm, romantic composition. Don't play your entrance too loudly, and listen to the phrases in the accompaniment so that you can imitate the expression given by the pianist. The *accelerando* in the 11th and 12th measures should be very subtle. Play the grace notes off the beat. The music of Chopin is a great study in lyricism.

GRIEG
Album Leaf

This dainty piece is from Lyric Pieces, Op. 12. You may wish to ignore the staccato markings in the beginning and play with a smooth legato. Many notes have a *tenuto* marking. These notes need an extra little push of air. You will need to work the bars with grace notes and sixteenths very slowly. The ritards should not slow down too much. Approach the music from a technical standpoint, learning the articulations and the exactness of the rhythms. The optional high G which occurs in measures 8, 32, and 56, is best omitted. Listeners will be better satisfied to hear a note played well. Do not risk the upper octave unless you are sure you can get it without a struggle!

DVORAK
Sonatina, Op. 100
Larghetto

You will want to play this piece slowly, and with deep feeling. Notice the notes with the tenuto markings, and give them a slight emphasis. Measure 28 is rhythmically difficult. Be sure the group of five sixteenth notes is played evenly.

Don't overblow the *sforzandos* near the end. Try to play this piece with tenderness. If you wish to play the last note without vibrato, do! This can make a very effective ending.

KREISLER
Rondino

You will want to sing your heart out when you play this famous encore piece! The saxophone can sound very much like a violin in this music. (Violinists envy the legato a saxophone can produce!) Try playing the grace notes in measure 94 with your side D key. The fingering for this is your regular C plus the high D sharp key without the octave key. This gives a very nice effect and makes it much easier. When you go from your fourth space E to high D it might be easier to keep the fingers of the right hand down on the E instead of lifting all of your fingers to get high D.

GRETCHANINOFF
Suite Miniature
Evening Waltz

You will need to practice this piece slowly, so that the dotted quarter and the eighth note in the second measure are given correct value. Work for a smooth, fluid legato. Ignore dynamics and interpretation until you can play the piece up to performance tempo. When you begin to play with expression, remember that this is a lilting, happy, Viennese waltz.

by Paul Brodie

COMPACT DISC PAGE AND BAND INFORMATION

MMO CD 4111
MMO Cass. 8021

LAUREATE SERIES CONTEST SOLOS
BEGINNING LEVEL FOR ALTO SAX

TUNING
Before the piano accompaniment begins you will hear four tuning notes, followed by a short scale and another tuning note. This will enable you to tune your instrument to the record.

GAVOTTE
from "Clavier Suite in G Minor"

JOHANN SEBASTIAN BACH

Cassette
Side B – Band 1 ♩ = 88 (1'22")
3 ♩ precede music

Band 1 – With Alto Sax
Band 12 – Accompaniment

Allegretto

MMO CD 4111
Cassette 8021

AVE VERUM

WOLFGANG A. MOZART
Arr. by Sigurd Rascher

Band 2 – With Alto Sax
Band 13 – Accompaniment

Cassette
Side B – Band 2 ♩ = 80 (2'50")

MMO CD 4111
Cassette 8021

HUNTERS CHORUS
from "Freischuetz"

Cassette
Side B - Band 3 ♩ = 96 (1'06")

CARL MARIA VON WEBER
Arr. by Rascher
Band 3 - With Alto Sax
Band 14 - Without Alto Sax

ANDANTE
from "Violin Sonata No. 1"

JOSEPH HAYDN
Band 4 - With Alto Sax
Band 15 - Accompaniment

Cassette
Side B - Band 4 ♩. = 80 (2'22")

Copyright © 1966 by Theodore Presser Compan, Presser Place, Bryn Mawr, Pennsylvania 19010
International Copyright Secured   Made in U.S.A.   All Rights Reserved   Used by Permission
Copies of the piano part are available from the publisher

INTERMEZZO

from "L'Arlesienne Suite No. 2"

GEORGES BIZET
Trans. by Harry Gee
Edited by Don McCathren
Band 5 - With Alto Sax
Band 16 - Without Alto Sax

Cassette
Side B - Band 5   ♩ = 80 (3'33")

MMO CD 4111
Cassette 8021

LARGO

CHOPIN
Trans. by E. Rousseau
Band 6 – With Alto Sax
Band 17 – Accompaniment

Cassette

Side B – Band 6 ♩ = 63 (2'34")

MMO CD 4111
Cassette 8021

ALBUM LEAF

from "Lyric Pieces, Op. 12"

Cassette

Side B – Band 7   ♩ = 88 (1'24")

·4 ♩ precede music

Allegretto e dolce

EDWARD GRIEG

Band 7 – With Alto Sax
Band 18 – Accompaniment

MMO CD 4111
Cassette 8021

LARGHETTO
from "Sonatina, Op. 100"

Band 8 – With Alto Sax
Band 19 – Accompaniment

ANTONIN DVOŘÁK

Cassette

Side B – Band 8 ♪ = 69 (3'16")

4 ♪ precede music

EVENING WALTZ
from "Suite Miniature"

Cassette
Side B - Band 9 ♩ = 192 (1'36")

A. GRETCHANINOFF, Op. 145, No. 10
Trans. by H. Voxman
Band 9 - With Alto Sax
Band 20 - Accompaniment

Tempo di Valse; moderato

RONDINO
on a Theme by Beethoven

FRITZ KREISLER

Side B - Band 10 ♩ = 188 (2'04")

Band 10 – With Alto Sax
Band 21 – Accompaniment

4 ♩ precede music

Allegro grazioso

MMO CD 4111
Cassette 8021

MMO MUSIC GROUP, INC., 50 Executive Boulevard, Elmsford, NY 10523-1325